Kai: ZLM

BE A BIRD-WATCHER!

17 birds to be found in this wordsearch puzzle!

blackbird   robin   jay   jackdaw   owl

swallow   swift   quail   wren   thrush

heron   lark   finch   tern   pigeon

dove   crane

c	r	a	q	j	a	y	w	r	e
r	a	q	u	a	i	l	l	s	p
o	w	l	l	c	r	a	n	e	i
b	l	a	c	k	b	i	r	d	g
i	a	c	k	d	i	d	o	v	e
n	r	s	w	a	l	l	o	w	o
c	k	w	r	w	r	t	e	r	n
f	f	i	n	c	h	h	s	e	r
i	n	f	c	h	e	r	o	n	s
s	h	t	h	r	u	s	h	s	e

ANIMAL HOMES

Can you find the homes for all the animals on our wordsearch list?
We've given you the first one or two letters for each one.

cat **b**

wasps **n**

eagle **ey**

wild rabbit **wa**

pet rabbit **h**

doves **co**

wolf **la**

fox **d**

moles **bu**

cows **by**

hens **co**

otter **d**

horse **s**

canary **c**

badger **se**

pet birds **av**

hare **fo**

dog **k**

pig **s**

bees **h**

sheep **pe**

a	s	t	b	u	r	r	o	w	a	r	e
s	t	d	a	m	a	i	r	i	e	h	o
h	a	e	s	o	b	y	d	l	a	i	r
a	b	h	k	e	n	n	e	l	i	v	e
v	l	u	e	n	w	e	n	r	p	e	n
s	e	t	t	m	a	v	i	a	r	y	r
t	m	c	s	t	r	e	h	f	o	r	m
y	y	h	b	y	r	e	f	r	m	i	n
b	s	c	o	t	e	c	c	a	g	e	t
y	c	o	o	p	n	e	s	t	t	e	t

VEGETABLE GARDEN

That's where you could find all the vegetables on our list.
Or, you could always fill in the missing letters, then find them in our wordsearch puzzle!

ca_li_l_w_r   art_c_ok_   _o_a_o   asp_r_g_s
_p_n_ch   sw_e_ c_rn   ca_b_ag_   _we_t p_pp_r
_p_ou_   p_mp_i_   _a_r_t   p_a   p_rs_i_
_ee_   gr_e_ b_a_

p	a	p	a	r	s	n	i	p	r	o	t
a	s	w	e	e	t	p	e	p	p	e	r
r	p	o	t	a	t	o	u	s	l	e	s
c	a	u	l	i	f	l	o	w	e	r	p
a	r	t	i	c	h	o	k	e	e	k	i
b	a	a	g	e	p	u	m	p	k	i	n
b	g	r	e	e	n	b	e	a	n	n	a
a	u	s	p	r	o	u	t	t	c	h	c
g	s	w	e	e	t	c	o	r	n	o	h
e	a	c	a	r	r	o	t	p	e	p	p

FARM ANIMALS

Lots of different animals to see on a farm!
Check the wordsearch list to see which you can find in the puzzle.

geese sheepdog pigs horse turkey donkey
ducks cockerel dog goat bull sheep
cat hens pony chicks

d	o	g	t	s	g	e	e	s	c
u	c	e	u	h	o	r	s	e	a
c	o	e	r	e	a	r	p	i	t
k	s	s	k	e	t	s	i	g	s
s	h	e	e	p	d	o	g	h	t
h	e	m	y	o	o	r	s	e	g
b	u	l	h	e	n	s	h	b	u
u	c	h	i	c	k	s	c	u	l
c	c	o	c	k	e	r	e	l	t
a	k	p	o	n	y	r	a	l	e

IN THE ORCHESTRA

That is where all the instruments hidden in the puzzle belong.
Fill in the missing letters first, then see if you can find them.

d_u_s t_mp_n_ _ou_le b_s_ c_l_o vi_l_
_i_li_ c_ar_n_t _ax_p_o_e fl_t_ o_o_
h_r_ _ic_o_o tr_m_o_e _r_m_e_
_ub_ p_a_o b_ss_o_ eu_ho_i_m

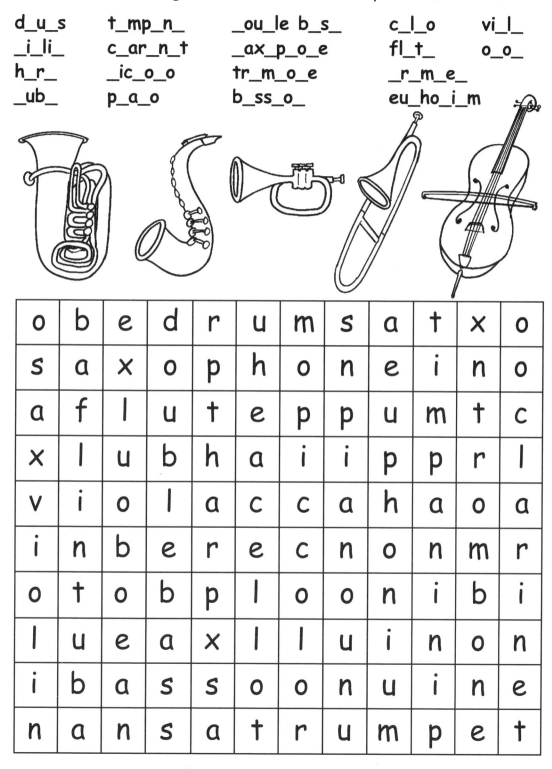

o	b	e	d	r	u	m	s	a	t	x	o
s	a	x	o	p	h	o	n	e	i	n	o
a	f	l	u	t	e	p	p	u	m	t	c
x	l	u	b	h	a	i	i	p	p	r	l
v	i	o	l	a	c	c	a	h	a	o	a
i	n	b	e	r	e	c	n	o	n	m	r
o	t	o	b	p	l	o	o	n	i	b	i
l	u	e	a	x	l	l	u	i	n	o	n
i	b	a	s	s	o	o	n	u	i	n	e
n	a	n	s	a	t	r	u	m	p	e	t

BE A CLOWN!

Check out the things you need from our list, then find them all in the puzzle.

custard pie   baggy pants   bubbles   funny hat
big boots   jokes   funny wig   tricks
       red nose   face paint   braces

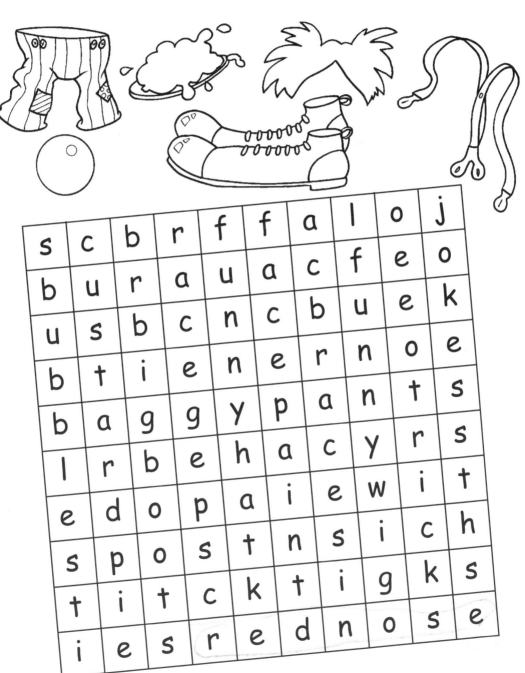

s	c	b	r	f	f	a	l	o	j
b	u	r	a	u	a	c	f	e	o
u	s	b	c	n	c	b	u	e	k
b	t	i	e	n	e	r	n	o	e
b	a	g	g	y	p	a	n	t	s
l	r	b	e	h	a	c	y	r	s
e	d	o	p	a	i	e	w	i	t
s	p	o	s	t	n	s	i	c	h
t	i	t	c	k	t	i	g	k	s
i	e	s	r	e	d	n	o	s	e

IN THE COUNTRYSIDE

How many different things would you see going through the countryside?
Fill in the missing letters, then see if you can find them in the puzzle.

wat_rf_ll   t_e_s   w_n_m_ll   si_np_s_   d_m
w_o_s   st_l_   br_d_e   st_e_m   c_n_l
_iv_r   _a_h   w_l_lif_   h_l_   v_l_ey
f_e_d_   _lo_e_s

w	e	r	w	a	t	e	r	f	a	l	l
s	t	w	i	l	d	l	i	f	e	s	s
i	s	l	n	w	a	r	t	p	a	t	h
g	e	b	d	o	m	i	c	a	f	r	e
n	e	s	m	o	r	v	a	l	l	e	y
p	b	r	i	d	g	e	n	i	o	a	m
o	r	e	l	s	t	r	a	m	w	m	e
s	t	i	l	e	h	i	l	l	e	r	s
t	r	e	e	s	i	l	e	s	r	t	e
r	e	f	l	f	i	e	l	d	s	e	r

PICK A PARTNER

Some words go together - king and queen, for example.
The partners to the words in this list are missing. We have given you the
first letter of each missing word. Can you find the words in the puzzle?

Tweedledum and **T**   bread and **b**   **n** and thread
hat and **c**   **k** and fork   bubble and **s**
cup and **s**   **P** and Judy   fish and **c**
soap and **w**   **s** and cream   salt and **p**
black and **w**   bucket and **s**   Jack and **J**
king and **q**   hands and **k**   **t** and chairs

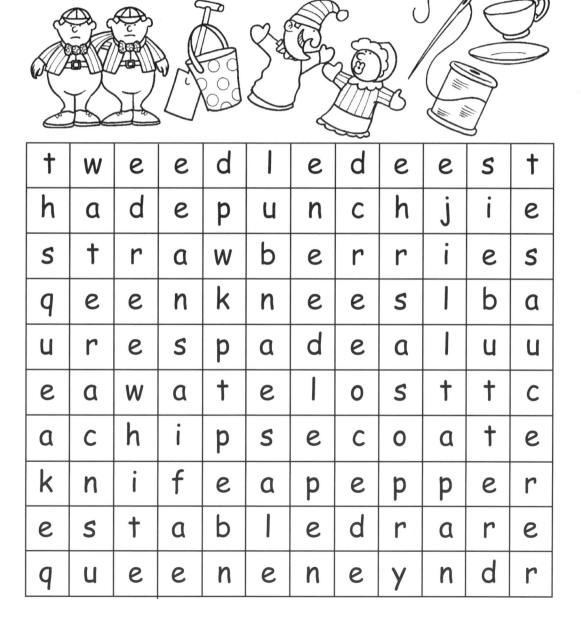

t	w	e	e	d	l	e	d	e	e	s	t
h	a	d	e	p	u	n	c	h	j	i	e
s	t	r	a	w	b	e	r	r	i	e	s
q	e	e	n	k	n	e	e	s	l	b	a
u	r	e	s	p	a	d	e	a	l	u	u
e	a	w	a	t	e	l	o	s	t	t	c
a	c	h	i	p	s	e	c	o	a	t	e
k	n	i	f	e	a	p	e	p	p	e	r
e	s	t	a	b	l	e	d	r	a	r	e
q	u	e	e	n	e	n	e	y	n	d	r

COME TO A PARTY!

What sort of party do you fancy?
Take a look at our wordsearch list of parties to find in the puzzle!

birthday   fancy dress   disco   sleep over   pyjama
street   fireworks   garden   internet   tramps
              tea   dinner   school

b	b	i	r	t	h	d	a	y	y
f	a	n	c	y	d	r	e	s	s
i	g	t	e	d	i	s	c	o	l
r	a	e	d	i	n	c	n	r	e
e	r	r	t	n	n	h	e	s	e
w	d	n	r	t	e	o	r	k	p
o	e	e	a	e	r	o	t	e	o
r	n	t	m	a	p	l	s	d	v
k	e	p	p	y	j	a	m	a	e
s	r	y	s	t	r	e	e	t	r

ON THE FARM!

That is where you could find everything hidden in the puzzle.
Read the clue and the first letter for each word on the list.

scares birds - **s**
used to turn the soil - **p**
it separates fields - **p**
where pigs live - **p s**
cows sleep here - **c s**
who works on a farm? - **f**

where crops grow - **f**
here hens live - **h   h**
a stack of hay! - **h**
farm machine - **t**
fruit trees grow here - **o**
field for animals - **m**

sheep, cows and pigs - **a**
grain is stored here - **b**
grown on a farm - **c**
barrier of trees or bushes - **h**
barrier - **f**
turkeys and chickens - **p**

o	r	c	h	a	r	d	e	c	o	t	s
r	s	c	a	r	e	c	r	o	w	p	f
p	t	a	y	p	a	t	h	w	m	l	e
i	s	n	s	o	t	h	e	s	e	o	n
g	f	i	t	u	e	b	n	h	a	u	c
s	a	m	a	l	d	a	h	e	d	g	e
t	r	a	c	t	o	r	o	d	o	h	r
y	m	l	k	r	y	n	u	m	w	b	n
p	e	s	a	y	h	a	s	s	h	e	r
c	r	o	p	s	f	i	e	l	d	s	s

BREAKFAST TIME

All the good things on the breakfast menu are hidden in the wordsearch puzzle.

toast   fruit juice   chocolate   tea   cream
porridge   cereal   grapefruit   muesli   jam
milk   sugar   egg   coffee   biscuit   marmalade

g	b	i	s	c	u	i	t	t	c
r	c	e	r	e	a	l	e	o	o
a	g	a	r	l	k	e	a	a	f
p	o	r	r	i	d	g	e	s	f
e	c	h	o	c	o	l	a	t	e
f	r	u	i	t	j	u	i	c	e
r	e	s	u	g	a	r	g	e	e
u	a	i	d	g	m	i	l	k	g
i	m	u	e	s	l	i	k	e	g
t	m	a	r	m	a	l	a	d	e

FANCY A NEW OUTFIT?

Start by checking through all the things on our wordsearch list!

pants	gloves	jacket	track suit	sweater	vest
shirt	socks	trainers	raincoat	anorak	shoes
	hat	trousers	jeans	shorts	

p	a	n	t	g	l	o	v	e	s
t	s	j	j	a	c	k	e	t	o
r	w	i	e	a	t	e	s	e	c
a	e	h	a	p	a	n	t	s	k
c	a	a	n	o	r	a	k	h	s
k	t	t	s	h	o	e	s	i	h
s	e	t	r	o	u	s	e	r	s
u	r	a	i	n	c	o	a	t	s
i	s	h	o	r	t	s	m	a	h
t	r	a	i	n	e	r	s	p	p

FIRST AID KIT

Check to see that all the things on our list can be found in the wordsearch puzzle.

antiseptic	safety pins	cotton wool	scissors
tweezers	medicine	ointment	bandage
plaster	gauze	gargle	lint
tape	cream		

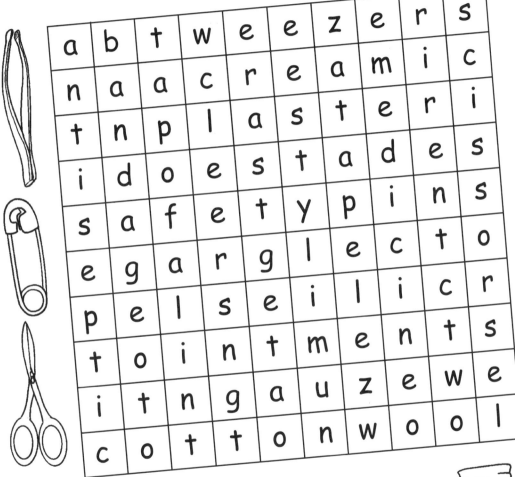

a	b	t	w	e	e	z	e	r	s
n	a	a	c	r	e	a	m	i	c
t	n	p	l	a	s	t	e	r	i
i	d	o	e	s	t	a	d	e	s
s	a	f	e	t	y	p	i	n	s
e	g	a	r	g	l	e	c	t	o
p	e	l	s	e	i	l	i	c	r
t	o	i	n	t	m	e	n	t	s
i	t	n	g	a	u	z	e	w	e
c	o	t	t	o	n	w	o	o	l

BAKE A CAKE!

All the things you need are hidden in the wordsearch puzzle!
Start by unscrambling the letters for each word on the list.
The first letter in each word remains the same.

mxingi blow   wodone snopo   arpon   caek tni   onev
forul   maganrrie   brutte   sltuansa   scaels
cadined pele   egg   anmlods   mlki   sgaur   sepic

s	u	l	t	a	n	a	s	p	i	c	a
p	i	m	i	x	i	n	g	b	o	w	l
i	c	e	m	m	s	c	a	l	e	s	m
c	a	n	d	i	e	d	p	e	e	l	o
e	p	r	f	l	o	u	r	a	s	t	n
g	r	a	i	k	b	u	t	t	e	r	d
w	o	o	d	e	n	s	p	o	o	n	s
o	n	s	u	g	a	r	o	o	v	e	t
s	m	a	r	g	a	r	i	n	e	o	v
w	e	t	c	a	k	e	t	i	n	e	s

ON YOUR BIKE!

Here is a list of bicycle parts. Fill in the missing letters, then find each part in the puzzle.

p_m_   pu_ct_r_ k_t   _udg_a_d   _ra_e_
l_m_   sp_k_s   fr_n_ f_r_   _efl_ct_r
_ea_s   l_gh_s   ch_i_   ha_d_e_a_s
_ad_l_   t_r_s   w_e_ls   b_l_   h_b

b	e	l	l	p	u	m	p	s	t	a	t
p	u	n	c	t	u	r	e	k	i	t	r
m	u	d	g	u	a	r	d	h	u	b	r
g	e	a	r	s	a	b	r	a	k	e	s
l	c	h	a	i	n	a	k	l	a	m	p
i	r	r	e	f	l	e	c	t	o	r	o
g	i	e	f	r	o	n	t	f	o	r	k
h	a	n	d	l	e	b	a	r	s	t	e
t	y	r	e	s	s	w	h	e	e	l	s
s	a	d	d	l	e	e	t	l	s	y	e

INDOOR GAMES

All the words listed below are games to be played indoors.
Fill in the missing letters first, then find them in the wordsearch puzzle.

b_dm_nt_n   b_sk_t_a_l   ta_le t_n_is   s_lit_i_e
i_e h_ck_y   ch_qu_r_   l_d_   ch_s_
b_lli_rd_   sn_ok_r   _quas_   p_o_
d_aug_t_   d_rt_   c_r_s

a	b	a	s	k	e	t	b	a	l	l	d
s	a	s	n	o	o	k	e	r	s	e	c
q	d	o	o	k	p	d	a	r	t	s	c
u	m	l	u	d	o	s	q	u	a	s	h
c	i	i	l	e	o	q	u	a	s	h	e
a	n	t	b	i	l	l	i	a	r	d	s
r	t	a	b	l	e	t	e	n	n	i	s
d	o	i	c	e	h	o	c	k	e	y	t
s	n	r	a	d	r	a	u	g	h	t	s
c	h	e	q	u	e	r	s	t	r	e	s

AT THE PLAY PARK

Everything hidden in this wordsearch puzzle can be found at the play park.
Fill in the missing letters first, then see if you can find each one.

s_e s_w   pa_d_i_g p_o_   fr_s_ee   s_n_ p_t
lid   _itt_r b_n   sw_n_s   b_l_
k_t_   _raz_ _ol_   b_w_s   _az_
g_m_s   _ou_d_b_u_

f	r	i	s	b	e	e	c	r	z	y	s
s	o	l	i	t	t	e	r	b	i	n	e
a	u	i	t	e	r	g	a	m	e	s	t
n	n	e	s	b	s	a	z	y	d	e	l
d	d	a	b	a	w	a	y	e	b	f	s
p	a	d	d	l	i	n	g	p	o	o	l
i	b	k	i	l	n	g	o	m	w	a	i
t	o	i	t	h	g	r	l	a	l	e	d
o	u	t	a	i	s	b	f	z	s	m	e
t	t	e	s	r	e	s	e	e	s	a	w

FOOTBALL MATCH

Find all the things on the wordsearch list, and it could be a great game!

goalkeeper	football	referee	kick	strip
player	penalty	pitch	crowd	rosette
linesman	teams	fans cheers	flag	boots

c	a	l	i	n	e	s	m	a	n
h	e	p	i	t	c	h	e	e	s
e	r	e	f	e	r	e	e	t	e
e	o	n	o	b	o	o	t	s	s
r	s	a	o	b	w	t	e	a	p
s	e	l	t	a	d	e	s	f	l
f	t	t	b	k	i	a	t	a	a
l	t	y	a	i	c	m	r	n	y
a	e	y	l	c	k	s	i	s	e
g	o	a	l	k	e	e	p	e	r

IN THE GARDEN

You could find all the things on this list in a garden - and they can all be found in the puzzle, too.

flower bed   deck chair   sun lounger   fork   trowel
border   flowers   hedge   grass   shrub
bush   edging   plant   shed   spade
rake   trug   hoe   lawn   patio

p	l	a	n	t	s	h	r	u	b
b	u	s	h	p	p	a	t	i	o
s	u	n	l	o	u	n	g	e	r
u	f	l	o	w	e	r	b	e	d
f	l	a	t	r	o	w	e	l	e
h	o	w	r	s	h	e	d	f	r
e	w	n	o	t	r	u	g	o	a
d	e	c	k	c	h	a	i	r	k
g	r	a	s	s	o	g	n	k	e
e	s	p	a	d	e	d	g	e	r

FAVOURITE CAKES

Is your favourite cake hidden in this wordsearch puzzle?
Unscramble the letters for each one, and find out! The first letter in each
word remains the same.

jma trat	madeeleni	moonacra	mereginu	gaetau
dtounugh	esccle	sisws rlol	snoecs	spoeng
boinwer	bettburnga	rmu bbaa	bnus	earcil

s	m	a	c	a	r	o	o	n	t	s	s
j	a	m	t	a	r	t	l	e	b	p	s
a	d	o	u	g	h	n	u	t	r	o	w
m	e	r	i	n	g	u	e	t	o	n	i
a	l	u	n	c	a	t	c	i	w	g	s
c	e	m	d	e	t	s	c	o	n	e	s
o	i	b	u	l	e	c	l	a	i	r	r
n	n	a	e	t	a	r	e	s	e	t	o
e	e	b	a	b	u	n	s	s	w	i	l
u	b	a	t	t	e	n	b	u	r	g	l

IN LANDS OF ICE AND SNOW

That is where you would find everything on the list of words waiting to be found in this puzzle!

sleigh   husky dogs   walrus   reindeer   polar bear
kayak   brown bear   penguin   sea lion   sledge
       igloo   Lapps   seal   Inuits

s	e	a	l	i	o	n	b	w	b
l	p	l	a	p	r	e	s	a	r
e	e	a	l	o	e	i	l	l	o
i	n	p	s	k	i	g	e	r	w
g	g	p	l	a	n	l	d	u	n
h	u	s	k	y	d	o	g	s	b
u	i	l	a	a	e	o	e	s	e
s	n	a	p	k	e	s	b	e	a
k	p	o	l	a	r	b	e	a	r
a	e	i	n	u	i	t	s	l	y

MAGIC ACT

All the things to make a fantastic magic act are hidden in this puzzle!
Fill in the missing letters for each word first.

g_o_es   s_e_l   ass_st_n_   ab_ac_d_b_a

c_oa_   _agic_a_   t_ick_   c_n_u_o_

r_b_i_   c_r_s   _ove_   m_g_c w_n_

_abi_e_   m_m_   t_p h_t   v_n_sh_ng a_t

g	l	o	m	a	g	i	c	w	a	n	d
l	i	c	a	b	i	n	e	t	s	t	e
o	v	e	g	l	o	t	o	p	h	a	t
v	a	n	i	s	h	i	n	g	a	c	t
e	r	i	c	o	n	j	u	r	o	r	r
s	a	s	i	n	c	s	p	e	l	l	i
a	b	r	a	c	a	d	a	b	r	a	c
a	b	i	n	e	r	t	c	l	o	a	k
m	i	m	e	d	d	o	d	o	v	e	s
i	t	r	a	s	s	i	s	t	a	n	t

CAPITAL CITIES

Do you know the capital cities of all the countries on this wordsearch list?
We've given you the first letter for each one.

United Kingdom **L**   France **P**   Scotland **E**   Eire **D**
South Africa **J**   Portugal **L**   Italy **R**   Greece **A**
Switzerland **B**   Denmark **C**   Bulgaria **S**   Egypt **C**
Agentina **B A**   Holland **A**   N. Ireland **B** Turkey **A**

b	u	e	n	o	s	a	i	r	e	s	s
p	a	i	s	c	a	i	r	o	a	k	e
a	m	s	t	e	r	d	a	m	b	a	d
r	b	e	l	f	a	s	t	e	a	b	i
i	l	c	o	p	e	n	h	a	g	e	n
s	o	f	i	a	r	o	e	c	m	r	b
b	n	l	i	s	b	o	n	a	i	n	u
e	d	u	b	l	i	n	s	c	b	l	r
j	o	h	a	n	n	e	s	b	u	r	g
a	n	k	a	r	a	l	o	u	r	g	h

FRUIT SALAD

You could make a tasty fruit salad using what you liked on our list!
But, can you find each of the fruits in the puzzle?

grapefruit   plum   pear   banana   olive   fig
raspberry   apricot   orange   lemon   strawberry
grape   melon   apple   lime   gooseberry

g	r	a	p	e	f	r	u	i	t
o	r	a	n	g	e	e	m	a	n
o	l	p	v	b	a	n	a	n	a
s	t	r	a	w	b	e	r	r	y
e	f	i	g	r	a	p	l	u	m
b	a	c	g	i	o	l	i	v	e
e	p	o	r	f	l	e	m	o	n
r	e	t	a	p	p	l	e	s	t
r	a	s	p	b	e	r	r	y	s
y	r	m	e	l	o	n	p	l	u

PEOPLE AT WORK

Read the clue and the first letter to find the job done by each person on our list.
Then find them all in the puzzle.

fights fires - **f**
goes on the stage - **a**
may help a doctor - **n**
mends frozen pipes - **p**
arranges flowers - **f**
plays an instrument - **m**

grows crops - **f**
makes meals - **c**
makes us laugh - **c**
helps us to learn - **t**
works to keep us healthy - **d**
looks after someone important - **s**

looks after our teeth - **d**
goes up in space - **a**
she serves meals - **w**

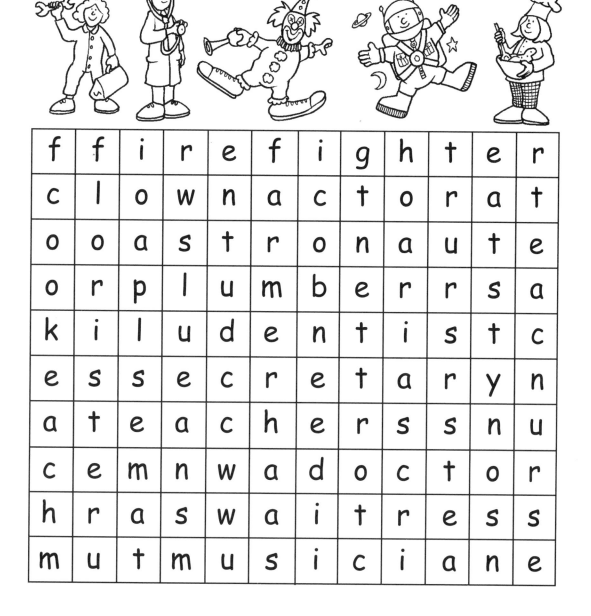

f	f	i	r	e	f	i	g	h	t	e	r
c	l	o	w	n	a	c	t	o	r	a	t
o	o	a	s	t	r	o	n	a	u	t	e
o	r	p	l	u	m	b	e	r	r	s	a
k	i	l	u	d	e	n	t	i	s	t	c
e	s	s	e	c	r	e	t	a	r	y	n
a	t	e	a	c	h	e	r	s	s	n	u
c	e	m	n	w	a	d	o	c	t	o	r
h	r	a	s	w	a	i	t	r	e	s	s
m	u	t	m	u	s	i	c	i	a	n	e

UNITED STATES

All the words in this wordsearch puzzle are the names of States in the USA.
Fill in the missing letters, then see if you can find them all.

Arkan_a_   N_w Y_r_   Cal_for_i_   K_nt_ck_
Neb_as_a   Ha_a_i   Ind_a_a   K_ns_s
T_xa_   V_rm_nt   Ala_a_a   Ma_y_a_d
A_izo_a   Mi_n_sot_   M_nt_n_   Ida_o   U_a_

u	m	n	c	a	r	k	a	n	s	a	s
h	a	w	a	i	i	e	l	a	n	r	m
a	r	e	l	d	i	n	a	s	e	i	i
v	y	r	i	a	z	t	b	n	b	z	n
e	l	f	f	h	t	u	a	h	r	o	n
r	a	u	o	o	c	c	m	l	a	n	e
m	n	t	r	i	z	k	a	n	s	a	s
o	d	a	n	e	w	y	o	r	k	y	o
n	o	h	i	n	d	i	a	n	a	e	t
t	e	x	a	s	m	o	n	t	a	n	a

ON YOUR FEET!

All these different types of footwear are hidden in the puzzle.

wellington	sneaker	shoe	trainer	ankle boot
slippers	clog	racer	slip on	plimsoll
sandal	bootee	creeper	flip flop	mule

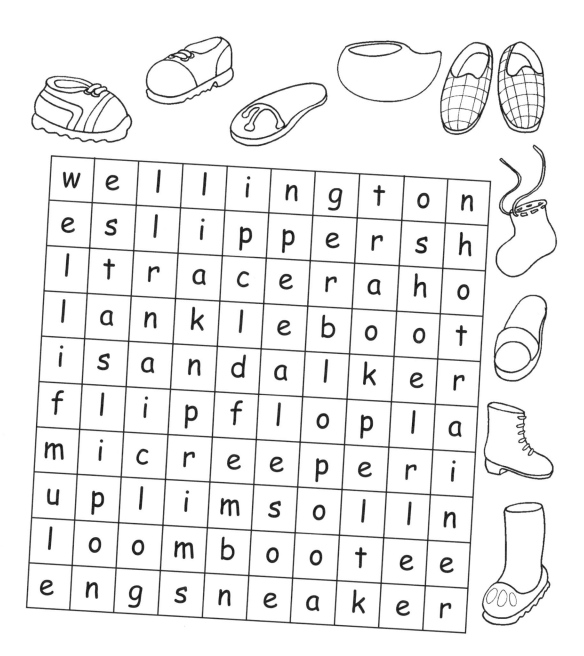

w	e	l	l	i	n	g	t	o	n
e	s	l	i	p	p	e	r	s	h
l	t	r	a	c	e	r	a	h	o
l	a	n	k	l	e	b	o	o	t
i	s	a	n	d	a	l	k	e	r
f	l	i	p	f	l	o	p	l	a
m	i	c	r	e	e	p	e	r	i
u	p	l	i	m	s	o	l	l	n
l	o	o	m	b	o	o	t	e	e
e	n	g	s	n	e	a	k	e	r

OUTDOOR GAMES

Is your favourite outdoor game hidden in this wordsearch puzzle?
Unscramble the letters for each one, and find out! The first letter in each
word remains the same.

voylleblla   bseablla   fotboall   glof   rubgy
tensni   crictke   rousdern   loacrsse
boswl   neatbll   hycoke   ploo

v	o	l	p	e	y	h	o	c	k	b	a
o	l	g	o	l	f	o	u	n	d	o	s
l	n	e	l	s	o	c	r	i	c	w	r
l	e	r	o	s	o	k	m	c	r	l	o
e	t	b	a	l	t	e	n	n	i	s	u
y	b	r	u	g	b	y	b	a	c	s	n
b	a	s	e	b	a	l	l	e	k	e	d
a	l	e	y	a	l	e	d	r	e	n	e
l	l	a	b	l	l	t	e	s	t	e	r
l	a	c	r	o	s	s	e	b	a	y	s

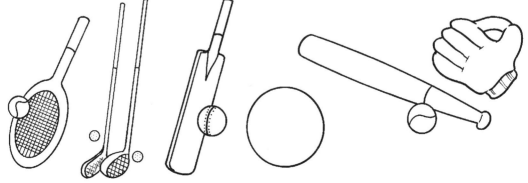

UNDER THE SEA

What could you find under the sea? Check our wordsearch list to find out - once you have unscrambled the letters! The first and last letters are correct in each word.

jlylsfeih - has stinging tentacles!
otesyr - may have a pearl inside
sae urhicn - not an earthly child!
suqid - squirts inky fluid
croal - can be part of a reef
seweaed - underwater plant
sgonpe -   use this in your bath
dveir - makes dives under water
turearse - lost by pirates?

agale - type of seaweed
srahk - dangerous fish
sae hsroe - not a real horse!
signtary - fish, can sting
oputocs - has eight tentacles
carb - can nip your toes!
palokntn - food for whales
calm - creature with a grip!

e	j	e	l	l	s	s	p	o	n	g	e
s	e	a	w	e	e	d	s	c	r	a	b
a	l	g	a	e	a	i	t	t	a	p	t
e	l	y	l	g	u	v	i	o	d	l	r
o	y	s	t	e	r	e	n	p	i	a	e
n	f	i	h	y	c	c	g	u	v	n	a
g	i	s	e	a	h	o	r	s	e	k	s
e	s	j	h	l	i	r	a	p	r	t	u
s	h	a	r	k	n	a	y	o	m	o	r
s	q	u	i	d	c	l	a	m	i	n	e

SPORTS PROGRAMME

There are lots of different sports hidden in this wordsearch puzzle!
Fill in the missing letters first.

gy_n_s_ics cyc_i_g s_i_m_ng f_nc_ng
h_ng gl_d_n_ k_r_te b_x_n_ ar_h_ry
sk_tt_e_ w_t_r s_i wr_st_i_g j_d_
_thl_t_cs ca_oe_ng

k	a	r	w	a	t	e	r	s	k	i	w
c	t	h	i	s	i	c	s	k	b	c	w
a	h	i	s	w	f	e	n	i	o	a	r
n	l	e	c	i	e	k	a	t	x	r	e
o	e	g	y	m	n	a	s	t	i	c	s
e	t	y	c	m	c	r	j	l	n	h	t
i	i	l	l	i	i	a	u	e	g	e	l
n	c	i	i	n	n	t	d	s	t	r	i
g	s	w	n	g	g	e	o	k	i	y	n
h	a	n	g	g	l	i	d	i	n	g	g

THINGS THAT GO

Unscramble each word first, then find them all in the puzzle.
The first letter in each word remains the same.

hodrofily   frie egnien   stocoer   cra   albunacem
loovctomie   apleroean   becylic   bsu   oli traken
morot beik   hteecropil   tmar   tixa   lryor   vna

t	r	a	m	b	u	l	a	n	c	e	t
a	a	h	e	l	i	c	o	p	t	e	r
x	m	y	r	o	r	y	l	o	r	r	y
i	t	d	b	i	c	y	c	l	e	a	b
a	e	r	o	p	l	a	n	e	i	v	u
s	c	o	o	t	e	r	o	f	o	a	s
c	o	f	i	r	e	e	n	g	i	n	e
c	m	o	t	o	r	b	i	k	e	n	t
a	o	i	l	t	a	n	k	e	r	e	s
r	n	l	o	c	o	m	o	t	i	v	e

RIVERS OF THE WORLD

Can you name the river which flows through each of the cities or countries on our wordsearch list? We've given you the first letter of each river to help you. Then find each river in the puzzle.

Kansas City, USA **M**
Rome **T**
Cambodia **M**
Ireland **S**
Vienna **D**
India **G**

USA (longest river) **M**
China **Y**
New York **H**
S. America **A**
Russia **V**
Israel **J**

Germany **R**
Paris **S**
Egypt **N**
London **T**
Glasgow **C**

m	m	i	s	s	i	s	s	i	p	p	i
e	i	t	e	j	o	r	d	a	n	v	e
k	s	h	i	e	r	h	u	d	s	o	n
y	s	a	n	i	l	i	e	a	h	l	i
a	o	m	e	k	o	n	g	n	a	g	l
n	u	e	k	o	n	e	i	u	n	a	e
g	r	s	c	l	y	d	e	b	n	u	b
t	i	b	e	r	h	u	d	e	o	n	e
z	e	r	a	a	m	a	z	o	n	s	t
e	z	a	r	o	z	g	a	n	g	e	s

TOYS

Find the letters for each toy on our wordsearch list hidden in the puzzle.

doll

drum

jigsaw

scooter

puppet

spinning top

toy soldiers

slinky

skittles

rocking horse

toy bricks

game

teddy bear

train set

tricycle

  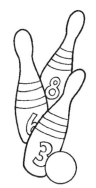 

t	o	c	s	c	o	o	t	e	r	l	e
r	o	c	k	i	n	g	h	o	r	s	e
i	s	p	i	n	n	i	n	g	t	o	p
c	l	u	t	e	d	d	y	b	e	a	r
y	i	p	t	o	y	b	r	i	c	k	s
c	n	p	l	i	n	t	s	g	s	d	e
l	k	e	e	j	i	g	s	a	w	o	w
e	y	t	s	d	d	r	u	m	r	l	m
r	s	t	r	a	i	n	s	e	t	l	r
t	o	y	s	o	l	d	i	e	r	s	s

POND LIFE

In the spring-time, you could find all the pond life on our list -
but can you find everything in the wordsearch puzzle?

waterweed   cygnets   frog   moorhen   spawn
toad   duck   coot   duckweed   swan
newt   water lily   tadpole   mayfly

t	t	a	d	p	o	l	e	g	a
o	u	s	u	m	e	i	f	o	c
a	m	o	c	m	a	y	f	l	y
d	u	c	k	o	f	f	r	o	g
s	w	a	w	o	s	p	a	w	n
w	a	t	e	r	l	i	l	y	e
a	n	c	e	h	c	y	g	e	t
n	a	o	d	e	t	s	l	y	s
e	w	o	y	n	e	w	t	a	e
w	a	t	e	r	w	e	e	d	d

OPPOSITES

Do you know the opposite for each word hidden in this wordsearch puzzle?
We've given you the first letter for each one.

interior **e**	forget **r**	decrease **i**	past **p**
common **u**	beginning **e**	question **a**	arrival **d**
maximum **m**	possible **i**	heavy **l**	large **s**
friend **e**	first **l**	speaker **l**	borrow **l**

e	n	t	e	n	d	i	n	g	a	r	l
x	t	e	r	m	i	n	i	m	u	m	e
t	p	r	u	u	n	c	o	m	m	o	n
e	r	d	e	p	a	r	t	u	r	e	d
r	e	m	e	m	b	e	r	s	t	l	t
i	s	l	s	y	r	a	n	s	w	e	r
o	e	i	m	p	o	s	s	i	b	l	e
r	n	g	a	e	n	e	m	y	s	r	e
e	t	h	l	a	s	t	r	a	r	e	r
y	e	t	l	i	s	t	e	n	e	r	e

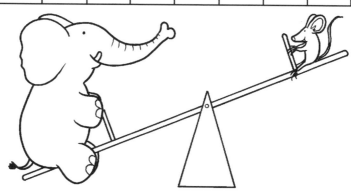

RAINY DAY

All the words to find on this wordsearch list are things to do with a rainy day.

mackintosh   waterproof   wet   umbrella

shower   rainbow   boots   raincoat

rain hat   puddle   cape   splash

rain   drain   raindrop

u	w	e	t	s	b	o	o	t	s
m	a	c	k	i	n	t	o	s	h
b	t	d	r	a	i	n	t	p	o
r	e	r	a	i	n	b	o	w	w
e	r	a	i	n	c	o	a	t	e
l	p	i	n	r	a	i	n	r	r
l	r	n	d	s	p	l	a	s	h
a	o	h	r	w	e	u	s	c	e
p	o	a	o	w	e	r	t	a	r
e	f	t	p	u	d	d	l	e	s

ON THE MAP

Each word hidden in the puzzle is something you would find on a map.
Fill in the missing letters first.

co_st_ine   _ou_t_in   m_t_rw_y   m_n_m_nt
oc_a_   b_r_er   is_a_d   g_lf
c_n_l   lat_t_de   l_nd   r_v_r
t_rr_t_ry   _ou_t_y   st_t_   t_wn
               co_n_y   _ong_t_de

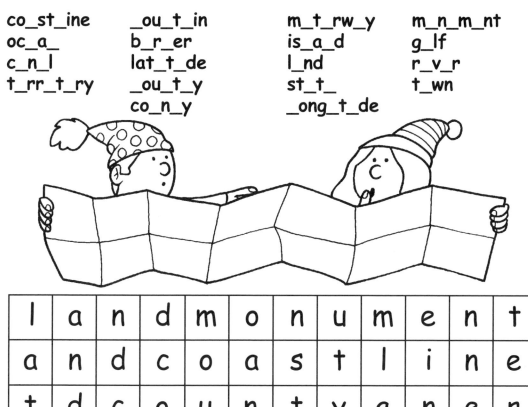

l	a	n	d	m	o	n	u	m	e	n	t
a	n	d	c	o	a	s	t	l	i	n	e
t	d	c	o	u	n	t	y	a	n	e	r
i	s	l	a	n	d	e	u	c	e	r	r
t	b	m	o	t	o	r	w	a	y	i	i
u	o	c	e	a	n	d	r	n	a	v	t
d	r	t	e	i	r	s	t	a	t	e	o
e	d	o	r	n	u	g	u	l	f	r	r
e	e	w	r	a	c	o	u	n	t	r	y
e	r	n	l	o	n	g	i	t	u	d	e

WHAT A FRIGHT!

Any of the things hidden in this wordsearch puzzle would be sure to give anyone a fright! Fill in the missing letters and find out!

f_ank_ns_ei_   sk_l_t_n   ph_nt_m hou_d   _am_ir_

gh_s_   _oot_t_ps   wer_w_lf   sk_l_

ec_o   d_a_ula   sc_ea_   s_rie_

w_tc_   gr_a_s   w_za_d   _oa_s   m_n_t_r

g	g	h	o	s	t	w	i	z	a	r	d
f	r	a	n	k	e	n	s	t	e	i	n
v	a	m	w	e	r	e	w	o	l	f	e
a	s	k	u	l	l	l	m	o	a	n	s
m	s	c	r	e	a	m	w	i	t	c	h
p	h	a	n	t	o	m	h	o	u	n	d
i	r	f	o	o	t	s	t	e	p	s	e
r	i	o	t	n	d	r	a	c	u	l	a
e	e	k	a	m	o	n	s	t	e	r	t
s	k	e	c	h	o	g	r	o	a	n	s

GOING BY TRAIN?

Each word on our list is something you might find at the station.
Fill in the missing letters, then find each word in the wordsearch puzzle.

l_c_m_t_ve   p_s_eng_r_   _lat_o_m   e_ca_a_or
t_ac_   _ig_a_ b_x   _or_e_   _arr_a_e
   _ruc_s   t_ck_t o_f_c_   e_g_n_ d_i_e_
     _hi_t_e   _nn_un_er   _n_i_a_or

p	o	r	s	w	h	i	s	t	l	e	p
s	i	s	i	g	n	a	l	b	o	x	a
t	r	a	c	k	a	t	r	u	c	k	s
r	a	e	s	c	a	l	a	t	o	r	s
p	l	a	t	f	o	r	m	o	m	m	e
o	r	i	n	d	i	c	a	t	o	r	n
r	c	a	r	r	i	a	g	e	t	e	g
t	i	c	k	e	t	o	f	f	i	c	e
e	n	g	i	n	e	d	r	i	v	e	r
r	e	a	n	n	o	u	n	c	e	r	s

ANIMAL SOUNDS

Can you say which animal makes each sound on the wordsearch list?
All the sounds can be found in the puzzle.

mew   trumpet   howl   gobble   bark   bleat
grunt   chatter   hiss   quack   crow   bellow
moo   bray   whinny   chirp   cluck   buzz   miaow

q	t	r	u	m	p	e	t	t	e
u	a	c	h	i	r	p	a	b	l
c	r	o	b	a	r	k	e	l	b
h	b	l	g	o	b	b	l	e	e
a	u	h	o	w	l	q	u	a	l
t	z	i	b	g	r	u	n	t	l
t	z	s	l	e	s	a	b	m	o
e	e	s	m	e	w	c	r	o	w
r	l	c	l	u	c	k	a	o	s
b	l	w	h	i	n	n	y	r	e

THINGS THAT FLY

Everything on this list flies in some way or another.
Can you find each one hidden in the puzzle?

aeroplane	kite	pilot	helicopter	bird
jumbo jet	glider	moth	parachute	balloon
butterfly	bat	airship	fly	

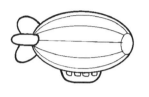

b	i	r	d	s	m	o	t	h	f
a	e	r	o	p	l	a	n	e	l
l	b	u	t	t	e	r	f	l	y
l	a	i	r	s	h	i	p	i	a
o	t	e	r	h	i	o	k	c	e
o	r	r	e	i	e	p	i	o	o
n	a	p	p	i	l	o	t	p	e
j	j	u	m	b	o	j	e	t	r
p	a	r	a	c	h	u	t	e	r
g	l	e	g	l	i	d	e	r	t

TREASURE CHEST

Can you discover all the treasure hidden in our wordsearch puzzle?

gold	coins	jewels	crown	silver
bracelet	necklace	rings	brooch	gems
diamonds	ornaments	casket	earrings	bangle

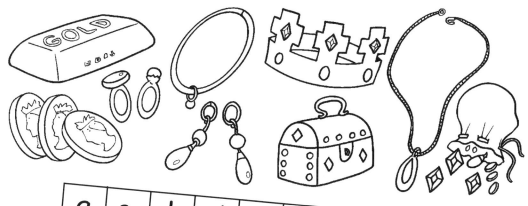

g	o	l	d	b	r	o	o	c	h
c	b	s	i	l	v	e	r	a	d
o	r	n	a	m	e	n	t	s	j
i	a	e	m	o	a	n	d	k	e
n	c	c	o	w	r	b	e	e	w
s	e	k	n	c	r	a	n	t	e
i	l	l	d	r	i	n	g	s	l
v	e	a	s	o	n	g	e	m	s
r	t	c	r	w	g	l	o	d	e
e	g	e	n	n	s	e	n	e	r

ALL KINDS OF BUILDINGS

Read the clue and the first letter for each building on our wordsearch list.
Then see how many can you find in the puzzle.

a big place for shopping **s**
books are borrowed here **l**
where you see paintings **a g**
a place for people to stay **h**
a place for students to stay **h**
where money is kept **b**
old things are displayed here **m**
adults study here **c**

where sick people go **h**
a place for knights in armour   **c**
children are taught here **s**
where things are made **f**
the Mayor's office is here **t h**
see films here **c**
see a play here **t**

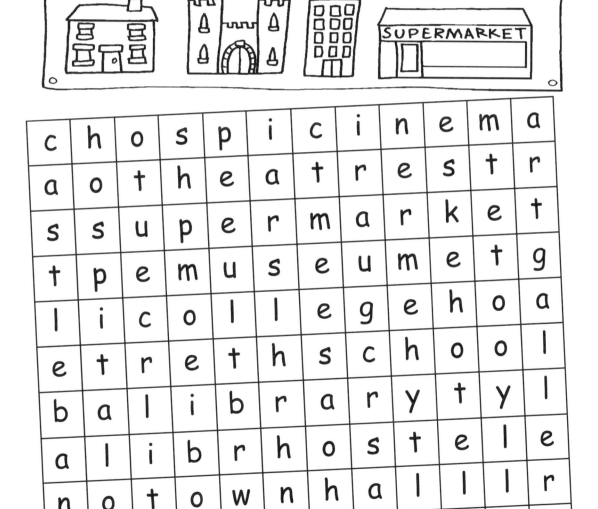

c	h	o	s	p	i	c	i	n	e	m	a
a	o	t	h	e	a	t	r	e	s	t	r
s	s	u	p	e	r	m	a	r	k	e	t
t	p	e	m	u	s	e	u	m	e	t	g
l	i	c	o	l	l	e	g	e	h	o	a
e	t	r	e	t	h	s	c	h	o	o	l
b	a	l	i	b	r	a	r	y	t	y	l
a	l	i	b	r	h	o	s	t	e	l	e
n	o	t	o	w	n	h	a	l	l	l	r
k	e	r	a	l	f	a	c	t	o	r	y

JUNGLE FRIENDS

The animals hidden in this wordsearch puzzle live in the jungle.
Follow the clues and use the first letter for each one to help you find them all.

has one horn - **r**
river horse - **h**
has hump - **c**
has famous laugh - **h**
'long neck' - **g**

king of the jungle - **l**
the largest ape - **g**
long-legged bird - **o**
striped horse - **z**
has trunk - **e**

eats leftovers of prey - **j**
does not change spots! - **l**
striped beast of prey - **t**
'almost human' ape - **c**
swings from trees - **m**

r	l	j	a	c	k	a	l	c	k	a	o
h	i	p	p	o	p	o	t	a	m	u	s
i	o	g	a	l	o	l	r	t	o	s	t
n	n	o	z	e	b	r	a	i	n	t	r
o	s	r	i	o	c	u	l	g	k	e	i
c	h	i	m	p	a	n	z	e	e	y	c
e	y	l	c	a	m	e	l	r	y	c	h
r	e	l	e	r	e	s	b	r	e	s	y
o	n	a	g	d	g	i	r	a	f	f	e
s	a	e	l	e	p	h	a	n	t	e	r

WINTER SPORTS

Can you find all the winter sports hidden in the puzzle? Unscramble the letters for each one first. The first letter in each word remains the same.

hskuy dgo raec   seiglh rnu   siking   boslbeigh
seped skaignt   iec deanc   cruglin   sik sallom
iec hoecky   soownbard   slegde   toobgang

h	u	s	k	y	d	o	g	r	a	c	e
u	s	k	y	d	o	s	k	i	i	n	g
s	p	e	e	d	s	k	a	t	i	n	g
s	k	i	s	l	a	l	o	m	c	e	s
c	c	u	r	l	i	n	g	o	e	c	l
e	t	o	b	o	g	g	a	n	d	k	e
y	r	t	s	n	o	w	b	o	a	r	d
e	s	l	e	i	g	h	r	u	n	e	g
b	o	b	s	l	e	i	g	h	c	h	e
o	b	i	c	e	h	o	c	k	e	y	s

WOODLAND ANIMALS

All the animals on the list are waiting to be found in this wordsearch puzzle.
Fill in the missing letters first!

fi_l_ m_u_e	f_x	d_rmo_s_	_qui_r_l
_e_g_h_g	b_t	w_a_e_	_a_er r_t
ch_p_u_k	v_l_	_ab_i_	_hr_w
_a_g_r	m_l_	st_a_	

r	c	h	i	p	m	u	n	k	f	o	x
a	h	i	t	s	h	r	e	w	i	t	e
b	w	e	a	s	e	l	s	h	e	w	t
b	a	t	c	e	d	e	v	o	l	e	s
i	t	h	v	o	g	e	r	x	d	g	e
t	e	m	o	l	e	a	t	e	m	o	l
a	r	e	r	a	h	r	s	t	o	a	t
q	r	r	e	d	o	r	m	o	u	s	e
u	a	b	a	d	g	e	r	u	s	t	e
e	t	a	s	q	u	i	r	r	e	l	t

PASTIMES

Is your favourite pastime hidden in this wordsearch puzzle?
Fill in the missing letters and find out!

h_rs_ r_d_ng   co_k_ry   ph_t_gr_ph_   sp_r_
ke_p_ng p_ts   cy_l_ng   r_a_i_g   _al_i_g
co_l_ct_ng   d_n_i_g   m_s_c   dr_m_
              cr_f_   a_t   _am_s

s	p	c	y	c	l	i	n	g	a	r	d
p	h	o	t	o	g	r	a	p	h	y	y
o	h	o	r	s	e	r	i	d	i	n	g
r	o	k	e	n	s	t	u	r	r	i	n
t	k	e	e	p	i	n	g	p	e	t	s
m	c	r	a	f	t	e	d	r	a	m	a
u	o	y	k	g	a	m	e	s	d	r	m
s	a	r	t	i	w	a	l	k	i	n	g
i	n	g	l	d	a	n	c	i	n	g	e
c	o	l	l	e	c	t	i	n	g	e	t

FIREWORKS PARTY

Lots of things for a great fireworks party are hidden in this wordsearch puzzle.
Fill in the missing letters, then see if you can find them all.

g_l_en rai_   _izze_   s_ow fus_   ju_p_ng j_ck
_p_rk_e_   _a_g_r   cr_ck_r   ro_an c_n_le
_o_k_t   m_sk   squ_b   wh_z_e_
_ir_wo_ks   g_y

c	r	a	c	e	f	f	i	z	z	e	r
g	g	o	l	d	e	n	r	a	i	n	o
s	l	o	w	f	u	s	e	e	f	i	c
p	j	u	m	p	i	n	g	j	a	c	k
a	n	g	a	r	b	a	n	g	e	r	e
r	s	u	s	q	u	i	b	a	n	e	t
k	q	y	k	e	w	h	i	z	z	e	r
l	i	i	f	i	r	e	w	o	r	k	s
e	c	r	a	c	k	e	r	m	a	z	t
r	o	m	a	n	c	a	n	d	l	e	e

FAVOURITE COLOURS

See if you can find your favourite colour in the puzzle.

red	khaki	blue	beige	green	gold
yellow	silver	mauve	purple	cream	grey
lavender	lime	black	white	pink	orange
		peach	amber		

y	e	l	l	o	w	h	i	t	e
e	l	c	i	r	b	l	a	c	k
l	g	r	m	a	p	e	a	c	h
g	r	e	e	n	e	s	s	k	a
p	e	a	v	g	a	p	i	n	k
u	a	m	b	e	r	i	l	r	i
r	y	a	l	m	a	u	v	e	g
p	v	l	u	o	g	r	e	y	o
l	a	v	e	n	d	e	r	e	l
e	b	e	i	g	e	d	b	e	d

GO CAMPING!

But first - fill in the missing letters of all the things to find in the puzzle.

di_h_s   t_n_   _ole_   p_n_   _u_k sa_k
_o_ch_s   p_g_   _am_   sl_e_i_g b_g   _o_es
b_a_k_t   st_o_s   s_ov_   _ill_w   cu_l_ry
g_ou_d sh_e_   m_squ_t_ n_t   w_t_r _ott_e

t	g	r	o	u	n	d	s	h	e	e	t
r	w	a	t	e	r	b	o	t	t	l	e
u	s	p	e	g	s	r	p	a	n	s	n
c	m	o	s	q	u	i	t	o	n	e	t
k	b	l	a	n	k	e	t	n	l	e	o
s	l	e	e	p	i	n	g	b	a	g	r
a	o	s	t	o	o	l	s	e	m	e	c
c	u	t	l	e	r	y	r	g	p	u	h
k	p	i	l	l	o	w	s	t	o	v	e
t	r	o	p	e	s	d	i	s	h	e	s

LOOK AFTER A HORSE

Everything you would need to look after a horse is ready to be found in this wordsearch puzzle.

grazing   harness   horseshoes   stirrups   grooming

rug   saddle   curry comb   grass   bridle

hay   bit   reins   brush

g	r	c	g	r	a	z	i	n	g
r	g	u	r	u	g	i	n	z	g
a	r	r	a	r	b	r	u	s	h
h	o	r	s	e	s	h	o	e	s
a	o	y	s	i	n	a	r	i	a
r	m	c	u	n	r	y	b	n	d
n	i	o	m	s	m	b	i	t	d
e	n	m	o	r	r	y	e	n	l
s	g	b	r	i	d	l	e	s	e
s	t	i	r	r	u	p	s	a	d

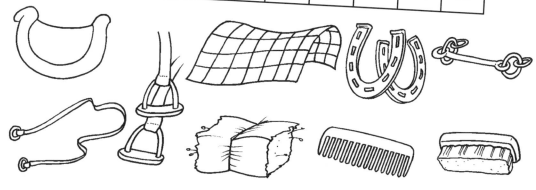

JOURNEY INTO SPACE!

and you might see everything hidden in this wordsearch puzzle.

moon   star   spaceship   meteorite   Uranus

Mercury   Jupiter   Venus   comet   Mars

astronaut   Earth   satellite   Pluto   sun   Neptune

u	r	a	n	u	s	m	o	o	n
m	a	r	s	s	m	m	o	r	e
e	s	p	a	c	e	s	h	i	p
r	t	l	t	e	t	u	j	u	t
c	r	u	e	v	e	n	u	s	u
u	o	t	l	a	o	r	p	c	n
r	n	o	l	s	r	e	i	o	e
y	a	o	i	t	i	s	t	m	r
r	u	n	t	a	t	r	e	e	s
t	t	h	e	r	e	a	r	t	h

SPORTS DAY

All the words hidden in this puzzle are sports day events.
Fill in the missing letters first, then see if you can find each one.

st_epl_ch_se   h_rdl_s   _gg a_d s_o_n
o_st_cle r_ce   j_ve_i_   h_gh j_m_
l_n_ ju_p   s_rin_   s_ck _ac_   d_sh
sh_t p_tt   p_le va_l_   r_l_y   d_sc_s

o	b	s	t	a	c	l	e	r	a	c	e
b	d	s	h	o	t	p	u	t	t	r	l
h	i	g	h	j	u	m	p	s	p	r	o
h	s	a	s	a	c	k	r	a	c	e	n
u	c	k	a	v	j	r	e	l	a	y	g
r	u	r	a	e	a	d	a	s	h	l	j
d	s	p	o	l	e	v	a	u	l	t	u
l	s	p	r	i	n	t	j	u	m	r	m
e	g	g	a	n	d	s	p	o	o	n	p
s	t	e	e	p	l	e	c	h	a	s	e

FIND A COUNTRY

All the countries in this puzzle begin with the letter A!
See if you can find them all.

Austria   Alaska   Antigua   Africa
Armenia   Angola   America   Argentina
Albania   Arabia   Australia   Andorra   Antibes

a	u	s	t	r	a	l	i	a	a
a	u	s	t	r	i	a	a	l	l
m	a	n	d	o	r	r	a	b	a
e	a	a	n	t	i	g	u	a	m
r	a	n	t	i	b	e	s	n	a
i	r	a	r	a	c	n	t	i	n
c	a	l	a	u	a	t	u	a	g
a	b	a	a	f	r	i	c	a	o
a	i	a	r	m	e	n	i	a	l
a	a	m	e	a	l	a	s	k	a

MIGHTY MACHINES

All the words hidden in the puzzle are names of big machines.
Fill in the missing letters, then see if you can find each one.

b_am eng_n_   st_am sh_ve_   t_nn_l b_rer
s_eam r_ll_r   tr_nsp_r_er   h_rv_st_r
    ran   d_g_er   ex_ava_o_   _ull_oz_r
       _ract_r   t_uc_   t_nk_r

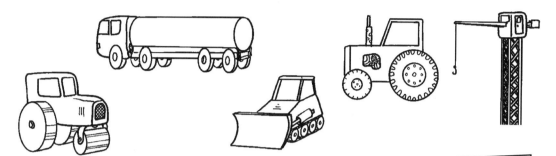

t	s	b	u	l	l	d	o	z	e	r	e
e	t	e	x	c	a	v	a	t	o	r	x
t	r	a	n	s	p	o	r	t	e	r	d
e	a	m	t	a	n	k	e	r	e	c	i
s	t	e	a	m	r	o	l	l	e	r	g
r	e	n	t	r	a	c	t	o	r	a	g
o	z	g	b	t	r	u	c	k	s	n	e
r	e	i	h	a	r	v	e	s	t	e	r
t	u	n	n	e	l	b	o	r	e	r	e
s	t	e	a	m	s	h	o	v	e	l	s

MOUNTAIN ANIMALS

All the animals hidden in the puzzle live in the mountains.
Fill in the missing letters, then see if you can find them all.

m_u_t_in g_at   m_rm_t   mou_t_i_   l_on
ll_m_   gu_n_co   ch_mo_s   b_ff_l_   w_l_
zeb_   i_ex   w_ld _x   ly_x   m_o_e
                       p_n_a   y_k   p_m_

m	o	u	n	t	a	i	n	l	i	o	n
a	m	o	u	n	t	n	p	w	o	l	f
r	o	p	a	n	d	y	a	k	a	l	o
m	o	u	n	t	a	i	n	g	o	a	t
o	s	m	w	a	z	e	d	u	b	m	o
t	e	a	i	b	e	x	a	a	u	a	t
m	t	r	l	d	b	u	z	n	z	e	b
m	a	r	d	b	u	f	f	a	l	o	r
a	e	s	o	s	t	e	r	c	h	a	m
l	y	n	x	c	h	a	m	o	i	s	e

SEA FISHING

All the fish hidden in the wordsearch puzzle can be found in our seas and oceans.
Fill in the missing letters first.

ha_ib_t   b_rr_c_da   s_rd_ne   m_ck_r_l   b_ss
p_ai_e   p_lch_r_   d_gf_sh   c_d   s_le
hak_   f_oun_er   t_na   spr_t   t_rb_t
d_b   wh_t_ng   _add_ck   m_ll_t   sk_t_

e	f	h	a	d	d	o	c	k	a	d	s
p	l	a	i	c	e	s	o	l	e	a	k
i	o	l	c	s	k	a	t	e	r	b	r
l	u	i	b	p	d	o	g	f	i	s	h
c	n	b	a	r	r	a	c	u	d	a	a
h	d	u	s	a	r	a	c	c	i	r	k
a	e	t	s	t	u	r	b	o	t	d	e
r	r	m	u	l	l	e	t	d	a	i	l
d	t	u	n	a	w	h	i	t	i	n	g
a	u	r	g	m	a	c	k	e	r	e	l

ONLY IN STORYLAND

Storyland is the only place you will find the people and things hidden in this puzzle.
Fill in the missing letters first.

m_n i_ t_e m_on   m_r_a_d   m_gi_   _ar_e_
_iz_rd   wo_der_a_d   _o_st_r   u_i_o_n   gn_m_
g_a_t   _ob_in   e_f   _air_   _ra_o_   kel_i_ i_p

m	a	g	i	c	c	a	r	p	e	t	e
e	g	o	b	l	i	n	r	k	l	p	e
r	i	l	w	o	b	l	g	n	o	m	e
m	a	n	i	n	t	h	e	m	o	o	n
a	n	i	z	k	e	l	p	i	e	n	s
i	t	n	a	r	p	e	t	m	y	s	t
d	i	d	r	a	g	o	n	p	e	t	y
w	o	n	d	e	r	l	a	n	d	e	s
o	n	d	e	l	u	n	i	c	o	r	n
n	d	e	r	f	a	i	r	y	r	y	s

SPARE PARTS

Spare parts of a car, that is! Unscramble the letters for each spare part,
then find them all in the puzzle. The first letter in each word remains the same.

weelh   wnidsecren   hbu cpa   ptroel takn
eginne   exsauth   listgh   boetnn
brumep   wnig mrrori   braesk   nmubre pelat
          gare bxo   raido   trey

h	u	b	w	h	e	e	l	t	o	m	e
u	b	w	i	n	d	s	c	r	e	e	n
b	o	n	n	e	t	c	r	e	x	l	s
c	a	t	g	r	a	d	i	o	h	u	b
a	n	u	m	b	e	r	p	l	a	t	e
p	a	l	i	g	h	t	s	t	u	y	n
p	s	b	r	a	k	e	s	e	s	r	g
g	e	a	r	b	o	x	t	x	t	e	i
b	r	a	o	b	u	m	p	e	r	e	n
p	e	t	r	o	l	t	a	n	k	s	e

WOULD YOU LIKE TO DANCE?

Lots of different types of dances to choose from -
and each one is hidden in this wordsearch puzzle.

conga line polka mazurka tap
tango jitterbug jive quickstep ballet
break square rumba samba disco
foxtrot waltz minuet barn

t	a	t	a	p	s	j	i	v	e
t	a	n	g	o	d	i	s	c	o
s	b	a	l	l	e	t	c	o	f
q	u	i	c	k	s	t	e	p	o
u	b	r	e	a	k	e	p	w	x
a	a	m	a	z	u	r	k	a	t
r	r	l	s	a	m	b	a	l	r
e	n	i	m	i	n	u	e	t	o
t	e	n	c	o	n	g	a	z	t
z	t	e	z	u	r	u	m	b	a

REPTILES

Dinosaurs were reptiles - cold-blooded vertebrates (with a backbone)
with scaly bodies, some of them with a hard shell.
How many can you find in this wordsearch puzzle?

turtle	tortoise	crocodile	terrapin	gecko
snake	chameleon	alligator	lizard	
caiman	dinosaur	tuatara	agama	

a	t	r	a	t	u	r	t	l	e
c	r	o	c	o	d	i	l	e	l
h	t	e	r	r	a	p	i	n	i
a	t	u	a	t	a	r	a	z	z
m	c	r	c	o	a	g	a	m	a
e	a	l	l	i	g	a	t	o	r
l	i	z	a	s	e	m	u	a	d
e	m	g	h	e	c	k	e	c	k
o	a	s	n	a	k	e	o	u	r
n	n	d	i	n	o	s	a	u	r

AT SCHOOL

Is your favourite lesson hidden in this wordsearch puzzle?
Unscramble the letters for each one, and find out! The first letter in each word remains the same.

laguagens   meamthatics   miusc   sceenic
stripcure   wokoword   crokeyo
exercesis   eshling   georapghy
hostiry   sortsp   atr
boolgyi   gmy

e	l	a	n	e	n	g	l	i	s	h	e
m	a	t	h	e	m	a	t	i	c	s	t
b	n	i	s	t	r	m	u	s	i	c	g
i	g	h	i	s	c	o	o	k	e	r	y
o	u	i	s	y	a	r	k	e	n	i	m
l	a	s	p	o	r	t	s	s	c	p	e
o	g	t	o	r	t	y	t	i	e	t	y
g	e	o	g	r	a	p	h	y	l	u	r
y	s	r	e	w	o	o	d	w	o	r	k
t	e	y	e	x	e	r	c	i	s	e	s

ON THE SEA

Here is a list of different ships and craft which have sailed on the sea, in the past and in the present. Can you find them all?

battleship	steamship	lifeboat	galleon	liner
trawler	frigate	sloop	barque	tanker
kayak	caravel	clipper	junk	raft

c	a	r	a	v	e	l	e	c	n
a	j	u	n	k	e	i	p	l	s
g	a	l	l	e	o	n	t	i	t
f	r	i	g	a	t	e	a	p	e
r	a	f	t	y	a	r	n	p	a
a	v	e	k	a	y	a	k	e	m
v	e	b	a	r	q	u	e	r	s
s	l	o	o	p	a	q	r	a	h
t	r	a	w	l	e	r	c	l	i
b	a	t	t	l	e	s	h	i	p

BE AN ARTIST!

You can find everything you would need in this wordsearch puzzle.
Fill in the missing letters first.

p_l_tte kn_fe   p_st_ls   o_l _ain_s   c_nv_s
ch_rc_al   _alet_e   br_sh_s   e_s_l
p_n_i_s   ch_lk   c_ay_n_   p_p_r
sp_n_e   _at_r   er_s_r

p	a	p	p	e	r	a	s	e	r	r	o
a	c	o	a	c	h	a	r	c	o	a	l
p	r	i	l	r	a	y	p	a	p	e	r
p	a	l	e	t	t	e	k	n	i	f	e
a	y	p	t	t	e	k	a	v	a	s	e
s	o	a	t	e	k	n	i	a	c	h	a
t	n	i	e	f	b	r	u	s	h	e	s
e	s	n	r	w	a	t	e	r	a	r	e
l	a	t	r	p	e	n	c	i	l	s	l
s	p	s	p	o	n	g	e	r	k	n	e

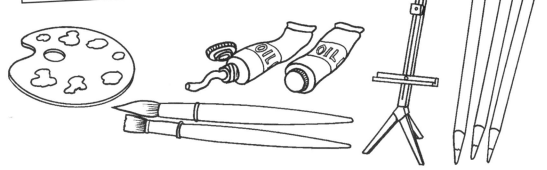

KNOW YOUR HERBS!

How many herbs do YOU know?
Check the list, then find them all in the wordsearch puzzle.

rosemary	marjoram	oregano	knapweed	sage
coriander	bay leaf	parsley	thyme	mint
	basil	dill	tarragon	

k	n	a	p	w	e	e	d	i	i
m	a	t	a	r	r	a	g	o	n
a	p	a	r	s	b	b	k	t	b
r	r	o	s	e	m	a	r	y	a
j	o	r	l	i	n	s	a	t	y
o	i	e	e	r	n	i	m	h	l
r	y	g	y	d	i	l	l	y	e
a	n	a	c	o	r	d	i	m	a
m	i	n	t	i	s	a	g	e	f
m	c	o	r	i	a	n	d	e	r

WHATEVER THE WEATHER

Lots of different kinds of weather to be found here!

rain	sunshine	sleet	ice	snow	thunder
cloudy	mist	fog	frost	storm	breeze
hail	windy	lightning			

r	a	n	d	f	r	o	s	t	s
a	s	e	i	c	l	o	u	d	y
i	t	o	r	m	s	s	n	o	w
s	o	m	i	s	t	h	s	t	i
n	w	i	l	a	h	h	h	f	n
s	t	o	r	m	u	a	i	o	d
l	i	g	h	t	n	i	n	g	y
e	r	a	i	n	d	l	e	a	i
e	e	l	s	l	e	t	l	o	c
t	r	r	g	b	r	e	e	z	e

ALL SORTS OF DOGS

How many breeds of dog do you know?
Fill in the missing letters, then see if you can find them all.

S_i_t B_r_a_d   _u_l_og   sp_n_el   r_t_weil_r
G_ea_ D_n_   _err_e_   _o_gi   _ox_r
_rey_ou_d   _ood_e   p_g   se_t_r
        L_br_d_r   a_gha_   _eag_e

b	o	x	e	r	a	f	t	e	g	l	e
o	x	p	o	o	d	l	e	s	r	a	s
p	u	s	e	t	t	e	r	t	e	b	r
s	a	i	n	t	b	e	r	n	a	r	d
p	f	g	h	w	e	l	i	c	t	a	a
a	g	a	e	e	a	s	e	o	d	d	n
n	h	n	p	i	g	e	r	r	a	o	d
i	a	b	u	l	l	d	o	g	n	r	e
e	n	l	g	e	e	r	r	i	e	t	r
l	s	t	g	r	e	y	h	o	u	n	d

ENTERTAINMENT

How many different types of entertainment can you think of? Unscramble the letters for each word on our list, ready to find in the puzzle.
The first letter in each word remains the same.

moilbe   pheno   cromupte   copmatc dcis   tevelsioni
raido   teahter   moiev caerma   teap ceasstet
cronect   vodei   fiml   DDV pleray   cineam   iodp

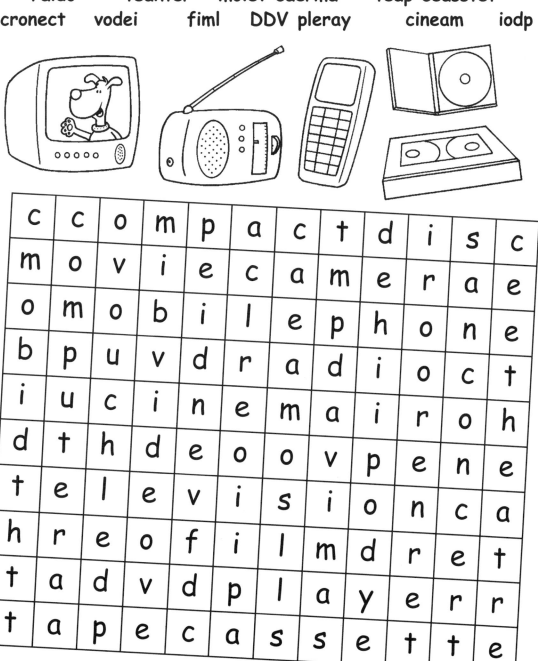

c	c	o	m	p	a	c	t	d	i	s	c
m	o	v	i	e	c	a	m	e	r	a	e
o	m	o	b	i	l	e	p	h	o	n	e
b	p	u	v	d	r	a	d	i	o	c	t
i	u	c	i	n	e	m	a	i	r	o	h
d	t	h	d	e	o	o	v	p	e	n	e
t	e	l	e	v	i	s	i	o	n	c	a
h	r	e	o	f	i	l	m	d	r	e	t
t	a	d	v	d	p	l	a	y	e	r	r
t	a	p	e	c	a	s	s	e	t	t	e

WILD FLOWERS

You probably won't find any of the flowers on our list in a shop -
but you will find them in the wordsearch puzzle.

bluebell   buttercup   daisy   dandelion
cowslip   coltsfoot   primrose   violet
           poppy   sundew

b	l	u	e	b	e	l	l	a	b
u	n	d	f	o	o	l	o	v	a
t	h	a	c	o	w	s	l	i	p
t	r	n	a	d	s	l	i	o	r
e	r	d	a	a	i	s	y	l	i
r	p	e	t	i	e	w	s	e	m
c	o	l	t	s	f	o	o	t	r
u	p	i	p	y	p	k	i	n	o
p	p	o	i	n	g	x	y	p	s
c	y	n	s	u	n	d	e	w	e

SUPERMARKET SHOPPING

Unscramble the letters for each word on the supermarket list, ready to find in the puzzle!
The first letter in each word remains the same.

csha restiger   chcke otu   spciale ofefr   cishear

wrei bsketas   basg   sceals   tolerly

diplsay   cenoutr   shevels   moeny

   bilsl   tsary   cnas   rpeceits   csah

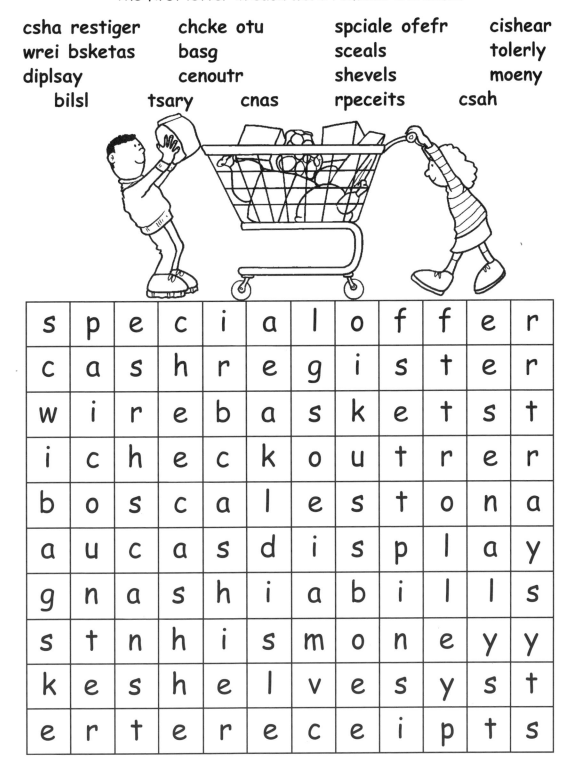

s	p	e	c	i	a	l	o	f	f	e	r
c	a	s	h	r	e	g	i	s	t	e	r
w	i	r	e	b	a	s	k	e	t	s	t
i	c	h	e	c	k	o	u	t	r	e	r
b	o	s	c	a	l	e	s	t	o	n	a
a	u	c	a	s	d	i	s	p	l	a	y
g	n	a	s	h	i	a	b	i	l	l	s
s	t	n	h	i	s	m	o	n	e	y	y
k	e	s	h	e	l	v	e	s	y	s	t
e	r	t	e	r	e	c	e	i	p	t	s

HOSPITAL VISIT

How many things on the wordsearch list would you see on a visit to hospital?
To find out, fill in the missing letters - then see if you can find them in the puzzle.

am_u_a_ce   st_et_h_r   wh_e_c_air   _oc_o_
_u_s_   cr_tch_s   t_o_l_y   p_t_e_t
sy_ing_   ch_r_   _isi_o_   _ub_c_e
   _urt_i_s   h_s_i_a_ b_d   th_r_om_t_r

s	t	r	v	i	s	i	t	o	r	w	e
t	s	t	r	e	t	c	h	e	r	h	e
e	c	r	e	c	r	u	t	c	h	e	s
p	h	o	s	p	i	t	a	l	b	e	d
a	a	l	c	u	b	i	c	l	e	l	e
t	r	l	a	m	b	u	l	a	n	c	e
i	t	e	d	o	c	t	o	r	u	h	s
e	s	y	r	i	n	g	e	y	r	a	n
n	s	c	u	r	t	a	i	n	s	i	n
t	h	e	r	m	o	m	e	t	e	r	t

COME TO THE CIRCUS!

You could see all the things hidden in the wordsearch puzzle!
Fill in the missing letters to complete the words first.

r_ng m_st_r   b_lanc_ng a_t   esc_p_l_gist c_o_n
m_s_ci_ns   t_gh_r_pe   h_m_n c_n_on
c_m_c c_r   j_gg_er   t_ap_ze   u_icy_l_

h	u	t	r	a	p	e	z	e	r	s	t
h	h	u	m	a	n	c	a	n	n	o	n
b	a	l	a	n	c	i	n	g	a	c	t
r	i	n	g	m	a	s	t	e	r	a	c
i	n	t	i	g	h	t	r	o	p	e	r
n	g	m	c	o	m	i	c	c	a	r	t
m	u	s	i	c	i	a	n	s	l	a	r
e	s	c	a	p	o	l	o	g	i	s	t
r	t	u	n	i	c	y	c	l	e	r	s
c	l	o	w	n	j	u	g	g	l	e	r

Solutions to wordsearches

PICK YOUR PET
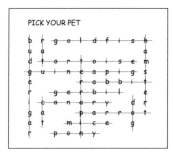

CREEPY CRAWLIES
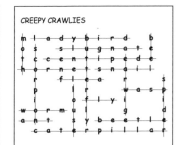

BESIDE THE SEASIDE
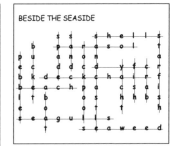

BE A BIRD-WATCHER!
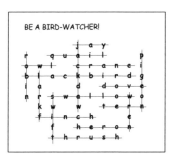

ANIMAL HOMES
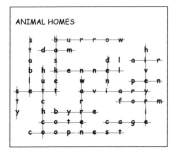

VEGETABLE GARDEN
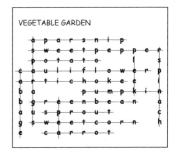

FARM ANIMALS
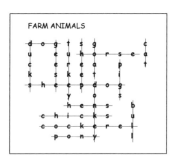

IN THE ORCHESTRA
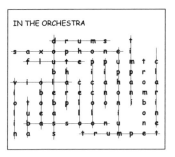

BE A CLOWN!
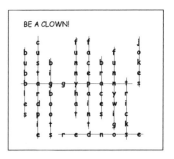

IN THE COUNTRYSIDE
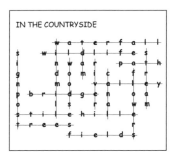

PICK A PARTNER
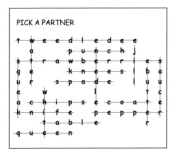

COME TO A PARTY!
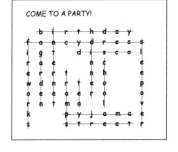

ON THE FARM!
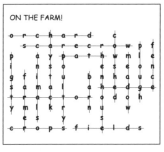

BREAKFAST TIME
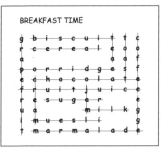

FANCY A NEW OUTFIT?

Solutions to wordsearches

FIRST AID KIT
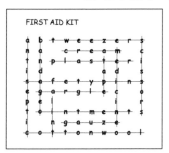

BAKE A CAKE!
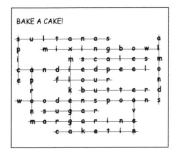

ON YOUR BIKE!
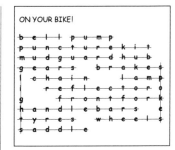

INDOOR GAMES
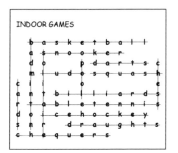

AT THE PLAY PARK
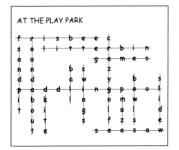

FOOTBALL MATCH
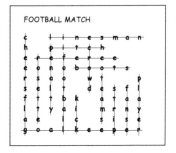

IN THE GARDEN
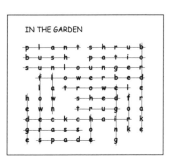

FAVOURITE CAKES
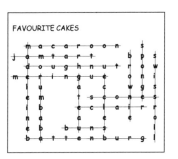

IN LANDS OF ICE AND SNOW

MAGIC ACT
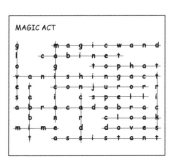

CAPITAL CITIES
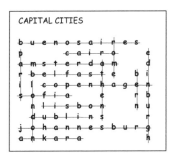

FRUIT SALAD
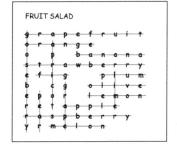

PEOPLE AT WORK
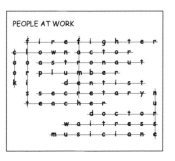

UNITED STATES
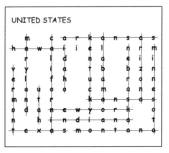

ON YOUR FEET!
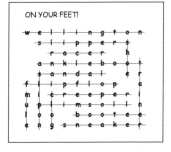

Solutions to wordsearches

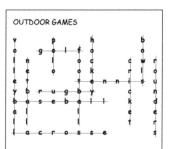

OUTDOOR GAMES

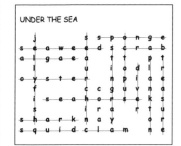

UNDER THE SEA

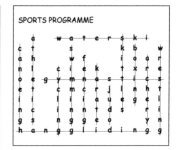

SPORTS PROGRAMME

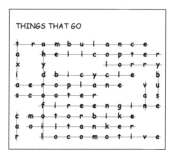

THINGS THAT GO

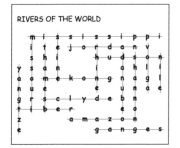

RIVERS OF THE WORLD

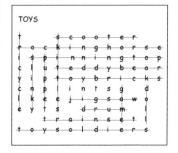

TOYS

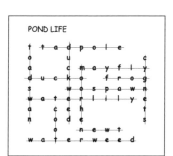

POND LIFE

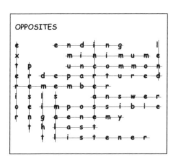

OPPOSITES

RAINY DAY

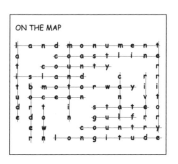

ON THE MAP

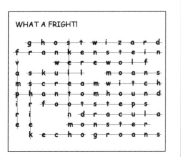

WHAT A FRIGHT!

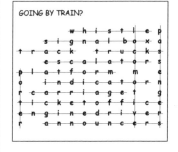

GOING BY TRAIN?

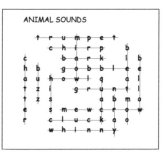

ANIMAL SOUNDS

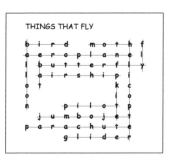

THINGS THAT FLY

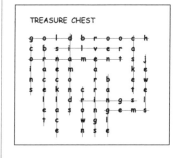

TREASURE CHEST

Solutions to wordsearches

ALL KINDS OF BUILDINGS
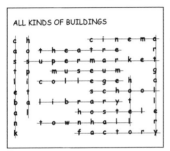

JUNGLE FRIENDS
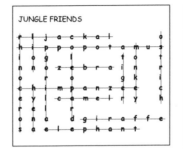

WINTER SPORTS
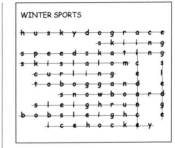

WOODLAND ANIMALS
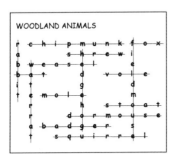

PASTIMES
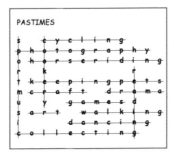

FIREWORKS PARTY
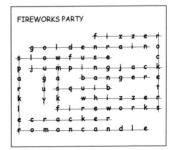

FAVOURITE COLOURS
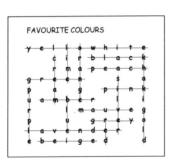

GO CAMPING!
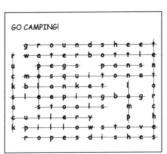

LOOK AFTER A HORSE
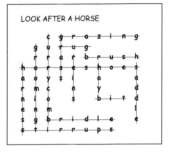

JOURNEY INTO SPACE!
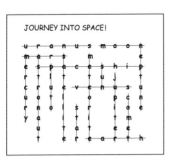

SPORTS DAY
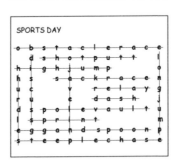

FIND A COUNTRY
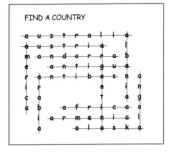

MIGHTY MACHINES
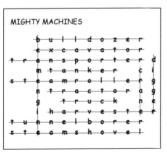

MOUNTAIN ANIMALS
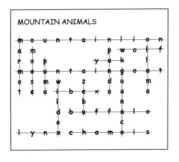

SEA FISHING
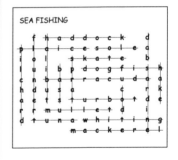

Solutions to wordsearches

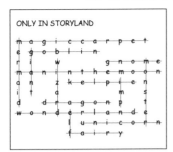

ONLY IN STORYLAND

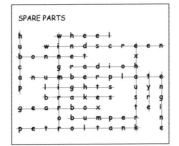

SPARE PARTS

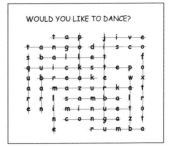

WOULD YOU LIKE TO DANCE?

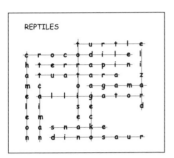

REPTILES

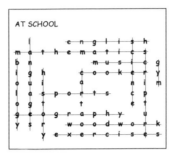

AT SCHOOL

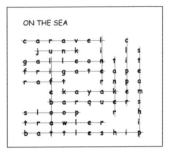

ON THE SEA

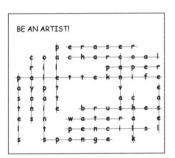

BE AN ARTIST!

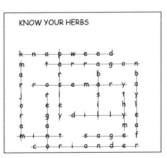

KNOW YOUR HERBS

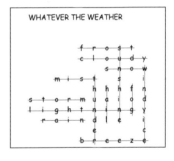

WHATEVER THE WEATHER

ALL SORTS OF DOGS

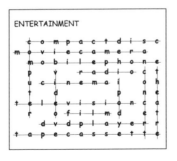

ENTERTAINMENT

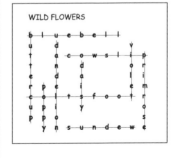

WILD FLOWERS

SUPERMARKET SHOPPING

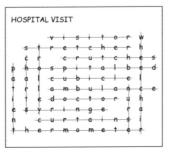

HOSPITAL VISIT

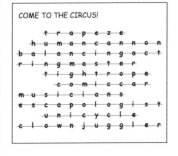

COME TO THE CIRCUS!